THE A&C BLACK SINGING EXPRESS SERIES

singing express songbook 3

ages 7-8

ANA SANDERSON
GILLYANNE KAYES
JEREMY FISHER

A&C BLACK • LONDON

Introduction

Singing Express offers a complete scheme for singing in the primary school: it explains how children's voices develop through childhood; provides the materials to support them with good singing experiences and it shows how to embed singing in the school day. This can all lead to a happy singing experience in school and, ultimately for life.

Singing Express is published in four volumes. **Singing Express 3** is for ages 7–8.

This collection of songs from **Singing Express 3** has been put together for music readers and music specialist teachers. The book and CD pack contains voice, piano and guitar arrangements in the book, together with audio performances on the CD. It is designed to be used alongside the **Singing Express** scheme or on its own, and is a useful reference and performance resource for the specialist teacher.

First published 2011 by A&C Black

Bloomsbury Publishing Plc

36 Soho Square

London W1D 3QY

© 2011

ISBN 978 1 4081 26578

Printed in Great Britain by Martins the Printers, Berwick upon Tweed

Illustrations © 2010 Christiane Engel

Sound recording © 2010 A&C Black

Cover illustration by James Watson

Edited by Stephanie Matthews

Designed by Jocelyn Lucas

Sound engineering by Stephen Chadwick

Music set by Jeanne Roberts

This book is produced using paper that is made from wood grown in managed, sustainable forests. It is natural, renewable and recyclable. The logging and manufacturing processes conform to the environmental regulations of the country of origin.

A CIP catalogue record for this book is available from the British Library.

contents

Song title	CD track	Page
PATTERN		
Singing all day	1	4
Big bad bug	2	5
Mirror, mirror	3	6
Dot to dot	4	8
Circle song	5	10
ENVIRONMENT		
What a load of rubbish	6	12
Just two feet	7	14
Traffic jamming	8	16
Who's that lurking in the log pile?	9	18
No home for the polar bear	10	19
MOVEMENT		
Jim along Josie	11	22
Chocolate, molinillo	12	23
Doodle oodle oodle	13	24
Noisy vintage car	14	26
We're on the move	15	28
Fancy Anansi	16	29
COMMUNICATION		
Sing bird	17	31
Done it	18	34
Neighbours	19	36
The telephone song	20	38
A message	21	40
Nonsense news	22	43
NARRATIVE		
Ozzie-oooo!	23	46
I got kicked by a kangaroo	24	47
Down by the bay	25	48
Who did swallow Jonah?	26	50
The green grass grew all around	27	52
Grandma's attic	28	54
PEOPLE		
Mrs Govinda Singh	29	57
I'm a great designer	30	59
Friends	31	62
Doctor, Doctor	32	63
The Tudors!	33	65
The bebop ballad of Boudicca	34	67
ACKNOWLEDGEMENTS		72

singing all day

CD TRACK 1

Words and music: **Barry Gibson**

Singing near the window,
   singing near the door. (scat)
Singing near the ceiling,
   singing near the floor. (scat)
Singing on the table,
   singing on the chair. (scat)
Singing on the bookshelf,
   singing on the stair. (scat)
Singing by the cupboard,
   singing by the wall. (scat)
Singing by the kitchen,
   singing by the hall. (scat)
Singing in the garden,
   singing in the shed. (scat)
Singing in the bath and
   singing in bed. (scat)
Singing all day and
   singing all night. (scat)
Singing's OK, yes
   singing's ALRIGHT! (scat)

SINGING EXPRESS SONGBOOK 3 © 2011 A&C BLACK PUBLISHERS   www.singingexpress.co.uk

Big bad bug

Words and music: **Helen MacGregor** (arranged for piano by Helen MacGregor and Michael Haslam)

There's a big bad bug
At the bottom of my bed,
Buzz buzz, buzz buzz.

There's a big bad bug
At the bottom of my bed,
Buzz buzz, buzz buzz.

Bug on a bed,
Bug on a bed,
Buzz buzz, buzz buzz.

I beg you bug,
Get off my bed,
Buzz buzz, buzz buzz.

Go sit on the rug,
That's the place for a bug,
Buzz buzz, buzz buzz.

Bug on a rug,
Bug on a rug,
Buzz buzz, buzz buzz.

mirror, mirror

CD TRACK 3

Words and music: **Helen MacGregor** (arranged for piano by Helen MacGregor and Michael Haslam)

Leader:
Mirror,
Mirror,
Mirror on
the wall.
Mirror,
Mirror,
Reflections of
us all.
Babe or gran,
Boy or man,
Big or small,
All:
You can see us all,
Looking in the mirror on the wall.

Echo:
Mirror,
Mirror,
Mirror on
the wall.
Mirror,
Mirror,
Reflections of
us all.
Babe or gran,
Boy or man,
Big or small,

Leader:
Mirror...

Dark or fair,
Curly hair,
Short or tall,
All:
You can see us all,
Looking in the mirror on the wall.

Echo:
Mirror...

Dark or fair,
Curly hair,
Short or tall,

Leader:
Mirror...

Wave goodbye,
Laugh or cry,
Stand or fall,
All:
You can see us all,
Looking in the mirror on the wall.

Echo:
Mirror...

Wave goodbye,
Laugh or cry,
Stand or fall,

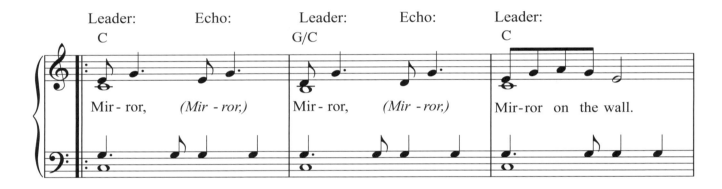

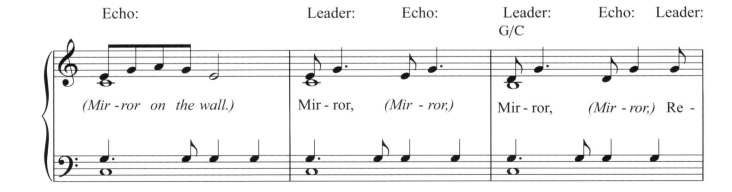

SINGING EXPRESS SONGBOOK 3 © 2011 A&C BLACK PUBLISHERS   www.singingexpress.co.uk

Dot to dot

Words and music: **Barry Gibson** (arranged for piano by Barry Gibson and Michael Haslam)

Dot to dot,
Place to place,
Spot to spot,
Through the space.
  What do they make?
  What's the shape?
  Dot to dot to dot.

Brick on brick,
Wall to wall,
Build them so,
They don't fall.
  What do they make?
  What's the shape?
  Dot to dot to dot.

(scat section)

Piece by piece,
Line by line,
Build our world,
Great design!
  What do they make?
  What's the shape?
  Dot to dot to dot,
  Place to place to place,
  Brick on brick on brick,
  Wall to wall to wall,
  Piece by piece by piece,
  Line by line by line,
  Dot to dot to dot,
  Dot to dot to dot!

circle song

Words and music: **David Moses** (arranged for piano by David Moses and Michael Haslam)

Walk round, hop around,
Make a circle on the ground.
Reach out, 'til you feel,
Someone's hand to make a wheel.

Circles indoors, circles outside,
Circles where you walk,
Circles where you ride,
Circles to eat, circles to throw,
Circles you can play,
Like an old banjo.

Walk round, hop around...

Circles in a pond, circles in the sky,
Circles of traffic wheels, going by,
Circles to draw, circles to spend,
Circles to go skateboarding,
With a friend.

Cir - cles in - doors, cir - cles out - side, Cir - cles where you walk,

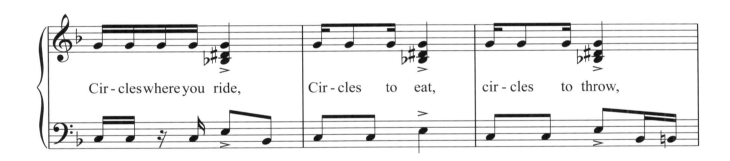

Cir - cles where you ride, Cir - cles to eat, cir - cles to throw,

Cir - cles you can play, Like an old ban - jo. with a friend.

what a load of rubbish

Words and music: **David Moses** (arranged for piano by David Moses and Michael Haslam)

What a load of rubbish!
What a pile of waste!
Is it past its sell-by date?
Don't you like the taste?
Is it old technology?
Is it out of style?
Take it to the dump
  and tip it on the pile.

What a load of rubbish!
What a pile of waste!
Do we have to keep it?
It takes up so much space.
Sort it out and save it,
Although it's old and grey,
It's a shame to lose it,
Recycle it and use it,
Some other day
But don't throw it away.

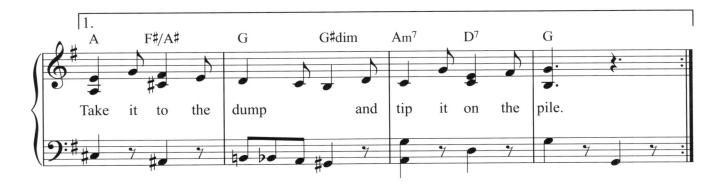

1.

A   F#/A#   G   G#dim   Am⁷   D⁷   G

Take it to the dump   and tip it on the pile.

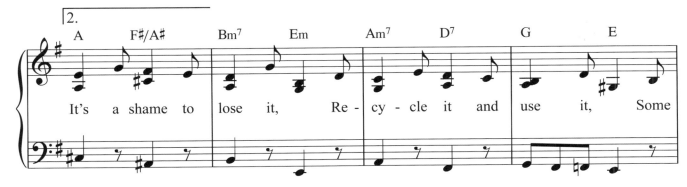

2.

A   F#/A#   Bm⁷   Em   Am⁷   D⁷   G   E

It's a shame to lose it,   Re - cy - cle it and use it,   Some

Am   Bm⁷   Am/C   F#/A#   D⁷(sus4)   D⁷   G

o - ther day But   don't throw it a - way.

Just two feet

CD TRACK 7

Words and music: **Em Whitfield Brooks** (arranged for piano by Michael Haslam)

How many pairs of shoes do you need
with just two feet?
How many lights to light your way
across the street?
How much food to fill up a fridge?
How many bricks to build a bridge?
How many pairs of shoes do you need
with just two feet?

How many miles in an aeroplane
when your home's alright?
How many times aboard a train
running through the night?
How much gas to fill up a car?
Why do you need to go so far?
How many miles in an aeroplane
when your home's alright?

How many pairs of shoes do you need
with just two feet?
How many lights to light your way
across the street?
How much food to fill up a fridge?
How many bricks to build a bridge?
How many pairs of shoes do you need
with just two feet?

SINGING EXPRESS SONGBOOK 3 © 2011 A&C BLACK PUBLISHERS   www.singingexpress.co.uk

How much food to fill up a fridge? How ma-ny bricks to

build a bridge? How ma-ny pairs of shoes do you need with just two

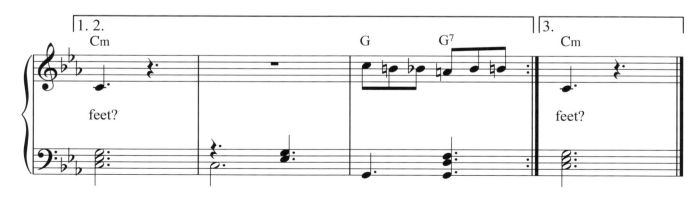

feet? feet?

Traffic jamming

Words and music: **Stephen Chadwick** (arranged for piano by Stephen Chadwick and Michael Haslam)

Cars and lorries,
Lorries and cars,
Speeds begin to drop.
Cars and lorries,
Lorries and cars,
Slowing to a stop.

Engines stuck in neutral gear,
Revving, revving, revving, revving.
No one's moving front or rear,
Traffic's jamming, jamming and the ~

Fumes are rising,
Fill the air,
No one's moving,
Going anywhere.
Fumes are rising,
Fill the air,
We are choking,
Do they really care? (x2 second time round)

**Traffic's jamming, traffic's jamming,
 Beep, beep, beep, beep,
Traffic's jamming, traffic's jamming,
 Honk, honk, honk, honk,
Traffic's jamming, traffic's jamming,
 Fumes are rising,
Traffic's jamming, traffic's jamming,
 Bop, bop, bop, bop,
It's no joke, we will choke.

Cars and lorries...

SINGING EXPRESS SONGBOOK 3 © 2011 A&C BLACK PUBLISHERS   www.singingexpress.co.uk

** For the 'Traffic's jamming' section divide the class into five groups, each learning one of the parts of the middle section: 'Traffic's jamming', 'Beep, beep', 'Honk, honk', 'Fumes are rising' and 'Bop, bop'. When the class is confident at singing the song with the accompaniment, these five ideas can be sung in any order and will all fit together.

who's that lurking in the log pile?

Words and music: **Barry Gibson** (arranged for piano by Barry Gibson and Michael Haslam)

Who's that lurking in the log pile?
Who's that lurking in the log pile?
Life's for living in the log pile,
That's what it's all about.

Fungus lurking in the log pile,
Growing and mouldering in the log pile,
Rotting and smelling in the log pile,
That's what it's all about.

Slow-worm lurking in the log pile,
Searching and slithering in the log pile,
Wiggling and wriggling in the log pile,
That's what it's all about.

Spider lurking in the log pile,
Spinning and weaving in the log pile,
Tickling and pouncing in the log pile,
That's what it's all about.

Millipede lurking in the log pile,
Burrowing and climbing in the log pile,
Chomping and chewing in the log pile,
That's what it's all about.

Who's that lurking in the log pile?
Who's that lurking in the log pile?
Life's for living in the log pile,
That's what it's all about.

Who's that lurking in the log pile?...

v 2. **Slower;** v 3. **Even slower;** v 4. **Faster;** v 5. **Even faster;** v 6. **Even faster still**

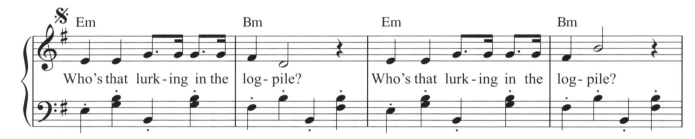

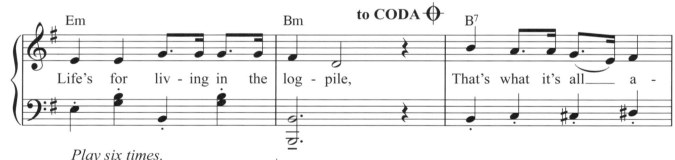

No home for the polar bear

CD TRACK 10

Words and music: **Stephen Chadwick** (arranged for piano by Stephen Chadwick and Michael Haslam)

I'm a polar bear, I'm a polar bear,
I'm a polar bear, I'm a polar bear.
Why don't you care?
I'm a polar bear, I'm a polar bear,
I'm a polar bear, I'm a polar bear,
This life ain't fair.

Because of all your carbon ways,
My polar land has hotter days.
Ohh ~
Your greenhouse gases really stink,
They make the ice crack and shrink!
Ohh ~
With every passing day,
My home is melting away.

I'm a polar bear...

Exhausted swimming round and round,
I long to walk on frozen ground,
Ohh ~
A tiny iceberg rescues me,
But takes me further out to sea,
Ohh ~
With every passing day,
My home is melting away.

I'm a polar bear...

I may look like a cuddly dude,
But man have I got attitude!
Ohh ~
Are you so blind you cannot see,
The way you live is killing me.
Ohh ~
With every passing day,
My home is melting away.

With every passing day,
My home is melting away.

SINGING EXPRESS SONGBOOK 3 © 2011 A&C BLACK PUBLISHERS   www.singingexpress.co.uk

Gb

ev - 'ry pass - ing day, My home is melt - ing a -

Ab

Bbm

Last time to CODA ⊕   **D. S. for Chorus and Verses 2 and 3**

way.   I'm a

⊕ **CODA**

With ev - 'ry pass - ing

Gb

Ab

day, My home is melt - ing a - way.

Bbm

Jim along Josie

CD TRACK 11
Words and music: traditional

Hey Jim along, Jim along Josie,
Hey Jim along, Jim along Jo.
Hey Jim along, Jim along Josie,
Hey Jim along, Jim along Jo.

Hop Jim along, Jim along Josie...

Tiptoe Jim along, Jim along Josie...

Crawl Jim along, Jim along Josie...

Run Jim along, Jim along Josie...

Play five times getting slower each time.
Last time very fast.

SINGING EXPRESS SONGBOOK 3 © 2011 A&C BLACK PUBLISHERS   www.singingexpress.co.uk

chocolate, molinillo

CD TRACK 12
Words and music: **traditional**

Chocolate, molinillo,
Corre, corre, que te pillo.
Correrás, correrás,
Pero no me pillarás.

(repeat x2, getting faster)

Play three times, each time a little faster

Cho - co - -la - te, mo - li - ni - llo, Cor - re, cor - re, que te pi - llo. Cor - re - rás, cor - re - rás, Pe - ro no me pi - lla - rás.

Doodle oodle oodle

CD TRACK 13

Words and music: **Barry Gibson** (arranged for piano by Barry Gibson and Michael Haslam)

Sing:

Doodle oodle oodle,
Doodle oodle oodle,
Doodle oodle oodle
Ooodle oo do DO.

Chant:

Doodle in the day and doodle at night.
Doodle in black and doodle in white.

Sing:

Doodle oodle oodle...

Chant:

Doodle in the kitchen, doodle in bed.
Doodle in blue and doodle in red.

Sing:

Doodle oodle oodle...

Chant:

Doodle with a pencil,
  doodle with a pen.
Doodling now and doodling then.

Sing:

Doodle oodle oodle...

Chant:

Doodle on paper, doodle on a pad.
Doodling crazy, doodling mad.

Sing:

Doodle oodle oodle...
(repeat)

NB: The recording of this song uses the keys of C, D, E, F and G. This version is in the key of D.

Noisy vintage car

CD TRACK 14

Words and music: **Stephen Chadwick** (arranged for piano by Stephen Chadwick and Michael Haslam)

I bought myself a vintage car,
It's powered by steam
  and looks bizarre!
But it makes the most amazing sound,
When the wheels go whirring round.
It's my hissing, chugging,
  noisy vintage car.

Chugg chugg, tappit tappit,
Ssshhhhhhh, clink clink,
Chugg chugg, tappit tappit,
Ssshhhhhhh, clink clink,
Chugg chugg, tappit tappit,
Ssshhhhhhh, clink clink,
Chugg chugg, tappit tappit,
Ssshhhhhhh, clink clink,
Hisssss, chugg-a chugg-a chugg!

I bought myself a vintage car...

Ch ch ch ch, bong bing,
  zzmm zzmm, click.
Ch ch ch ch, bong bing,
  zzmm zzmm, click.
Ch ch ch ch, bong bing,
  zzmm zzmm, click.
Ch ch ch ch, bong bing,
  zzmm zzmm, click.
Hisssss, chug-ga chug-ga chugg!

I bought myself a vintage car...

we're on the move

Words and music: **David Moses** (arranged for piano by David Moses and Michael Haslam)

We're on the move, packing up to go,
What will it be like? I don't know.
Will there be a lift that's
old and slow?
Will we look down on the
world below?

We're on the move, packing up to go,
What will it be like? I don't know.
Will there be a garden,
green in spring?
Where I can play on a garden swing?

We're on the move, packing up to go,
What will it be like? I don't know.
Will there be a pavement,
smooth and hard?
Will there be pigs in the
farmer's yard?

We're on the move, packing up to go,
What will it be like? I don't know.
Who will be the people
we shall meet?
Maybe new friends will live
in our street.

Packed all my toys, a toothbrush
and a comb,
I'll always remember our old home.

Fancy Anansi

CD TRACK 16

Words and music: **David Moses** (arranged for piano by David Moses and Michael Haslam)

Jump, jump, jump, jump,
Jump, jump, jump, jump,
Land on the floor
With a great big bump,
   Fancy Anansi, clever little spider,
   Fancy Anansi, clever little man.

Hop, hop, hop, hop,
Hop, hop, hop, hop,
Hiding in the garden
OUT YOU POP!
   Fancy Anansi, clever little spider,
   Fancy Anansi, clever little man.

Creep, creep around,
Creep, creep around,
Scurry like a spider
Along the ground,
   Fancy Anansi, clever little spider,
   Fancy Anansi, clever little man.

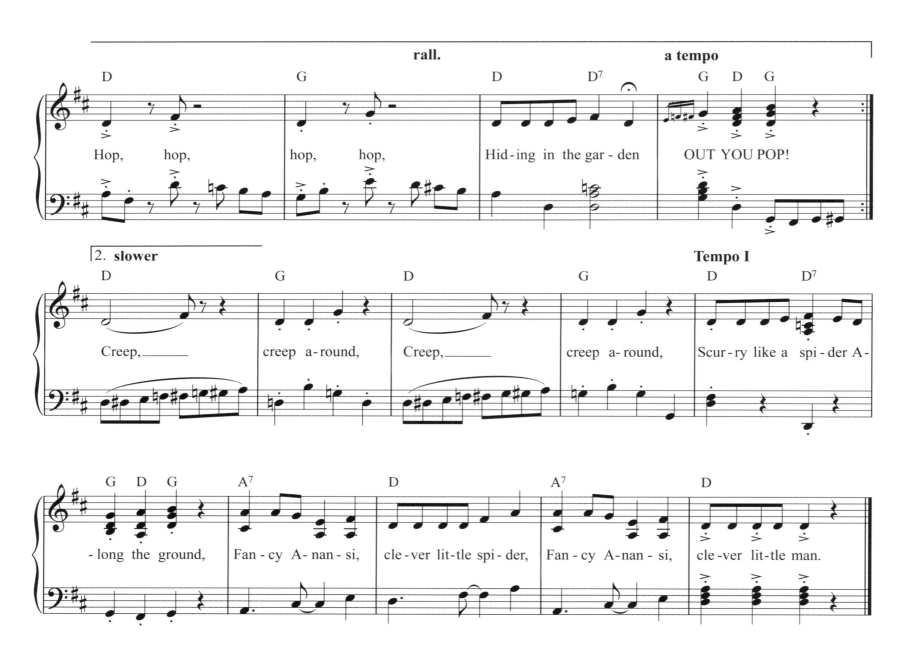

Hop,   hop,   hop,   hop,   Hid-ing in the gar-den   OUT YOU POP!

2. slower

Creep,_____   creep a-round,   Creep,_____   creep a-round,   Scur-ry like a spi-der A-

-long the ground,   Fan-cy A-nan-si,   cle-ver lit-tle spi-der,   Fan-cy A-nan-si,   cle-ver lit-tle man.

SINGING EXPRESS SONGBOOK 3 © 2011 A&C BLACK PUBLISHERS   www.singingexpress.co.uk

sing bird

CD TRACK 17

Words and music: **Barry Gibson** (arranged for piano by Barry Gibson and Michael Haslam)

Sing bird, sing bird, sing out loud!
So you stand out from the crowd.
Sing out bright and strong and proud.
Sing bird, sing bird, sing out loud!

Stake a claim on bush or tree,
Make it yours for all to see.
There's no time to let it be,
Sing bird, sing bird, sing out loud!

Sing bird, sing bird, sing out loud...

Spring won't wait,
   so build that nest,
Show who's who
   and show who's best.
Find a mate, keep out the rest!
Sing bird, sing bird, sing out loud!

Sing bird, sing bird, sing out loud...

Time moves on and eggs soon hatch,
Mouths to feed and food to catch.
Home sweet home,
   defend your patch,
Sing bird, sing bird, sing out loud!

Sing bird, sing bird, sing out loud...

(repeat)

With vigour

NB: The recording of this song uses the keys of C, D and E♭ with a double-chorus to end.

This version is in the key of D.

SINGING EXPRESS SONGBOOK 3 © 2011 A&C BLACK PUBLISHERS   **www.singingexpress.co.uk**

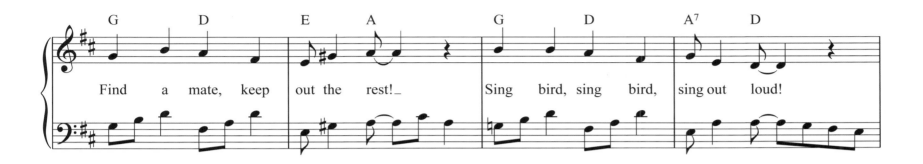

CHORUS *Play once after verse 2 and twice after verse 3*

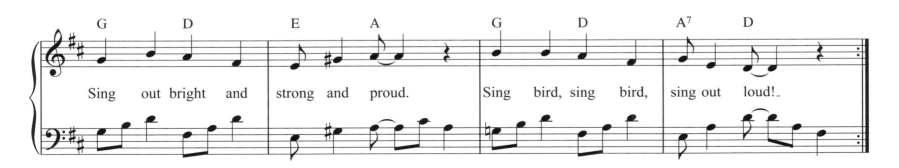

Done it

CD TRACK 18

Words and music: **Matthew White and Ana Sanderson**

Group 1:

Get up now, or you'll be late,
Eat your breakfast, clear your plate.
Are you ready?
We've got lots to do.

Group 2:

I've got up, I won't be late,
Had my breakfast, cleared my plate.
I'm ready as I'll ever be,
Wait a moment, count to three,
Is there time to say 'Good morning'?

Group 1:

Flush the toilet, brush your hair,
Have you changed your underwear?
Are you ready?
We've got lots to do.

Group 2:

Flushed the toilet, brushed my hair,
Yes, I've changed my underwear.
I'm ready as I'll ever be,
Wait a moment, count to three,
Is there time to say 'I'm sorry'?

Group 1:

Put your rucksack on your back,
Always take a healthy snack.
Are you ready?
We've got lots to do.

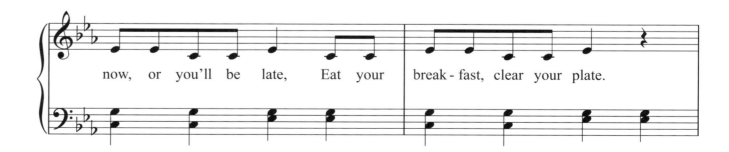

Group 2:

Yes, my rucksack's on my back,
And I've got a healthy snack.
I'm ready as I'll ever be,
Wait a moment, count to three,
Is there time to say 'I'm late now'?

Neighbours

CD TRACK 19

Words and music: **Sue Nicholls** (arranged for piano by Sue Nicholls and Michael Haslam)

Group 1:

I don't think we've met before,
So I'm knock, knock, knocking
at your front door.

Group 2:

Don't come in, I've got the flu,
Could you try the neighbours
at Number Two?

Group 1:

I don't think we've met before...

Group 2:

Don't come in, I've made the tea,
Could you try the neighbours
at Number Three?

Group 1:

I don't think we've met before...

Group 2:

Don't come in, I've washed the floor,
Could you try the neighbours
at Number Four?

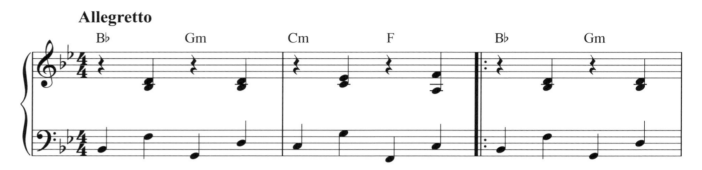

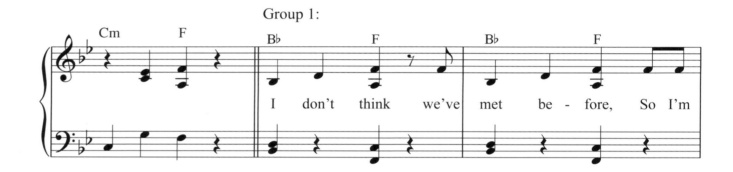

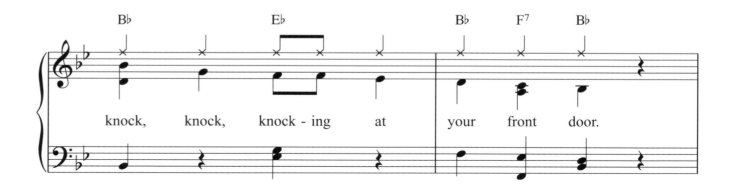

Group 1:
I don't think we've met before...

Group 2:
Don't come in, I've swept the drive,
Could you try the neighbours
   at Number Five?

All:
I've just moved, it's good to meet you,
Now I'm off to see the neighbours
   in our street!

Group 2:

Don't   come   in,   I've   got   the   flu,   Could   you

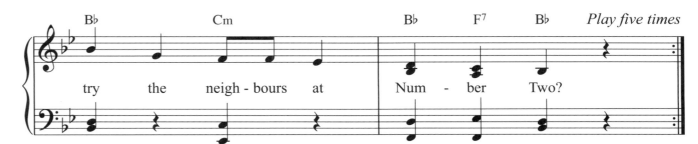

try   the   neigh - bours   at   Num - ber   Two?   *Play five times*

The telephone Song

CD TRACK 20

Words and music: **traditional**

(On 'click', click your fingers)

Group 1: **Hey Kaz,**

Group 2: *I hear you calling my name.*

Group 1: **Hey Kaz,**

Group 2: *I hear you calling again.*

Group 1: **There's someone on the telephone.**

Group 2: *If that's Matthew then I'm not at home.*

All: **With a rick** (click)
          tick ticketty tick, oh yeah!
          With a rick (click)
          tick ticketty tick.

Group 2: **Hey Mohammed,**

Group 3: *I hear you calling my name.*

Group 2: **Hey Mohammed,**

Group 3: *I hear you calling again.*

Group 2: **There's someone on the telephone.**

Group 3: *If that's Chloë then I'm not at home.*

Straight quavers

Swung quavers

Group 1: Hey Kaz,___ Group 2: I hear you call-ing my name. Group 1: Hey

Group 2: Kaz,___ I hear you call-ing a-gain. Group 1: There's some-one on the

SINGING EXPRESS SONGBOOK 3 © 2011 A&C BLACK PUBLISHERS   www.singingexpress.co.uk

All: **With a rick** (click)
tick ticketty tick, oh yeah!
With a rick (click)
tick ticketty tick.

Group 3: **Hey Steven,**
Group 1: *I hear you calling my name.*
Group 3: **Hey Steven,**
Group 1: *I hear you calling again.*
Group 3: **There's someone on the
telephone.**
Group 1: *If that's Paula then I'm
not at home.*

All: **With a rick** (click)
tick ticketty tick, oh yeah!
With a rick (click)
tick ticketty tick.

A message

CD TRACK 21

Words and music: **Barry Gibson** (arranged for piano by Barry Gibson and Michael Haslam)

A message, a message!
I've got to send a message.
Sing it? Or say it?
Beat a drum and play it?
Text a text? Or fax a fax?
Blow it on an alto sax?
A message, a message!
I've got to send a message today!

A message, a message!
I've got to send a message.
Email by computer?
Honk it on a hooter?
Secret-code it? Beep beep beep.
Mobile-phone it? Bleep bleep bleep.
A message, a message!
I've got to send a message today!

1 2 3 4 knock that rhythm on the door!
(tap a rhythm)
2 4 6 8 make signals that communicate!
(communication sound effects)

A message, a message!

I've got to send a message.
Semaphore flags in the air?
Torches flashing here to there?
Online-chat or blog-o-sphere?
Digits dashing there to here?
A message, a message!
I've got to send a message today!

A message, a message!
I've got to send a message.
Picture-postcard, snail-mail?
Parcel over road and rail?
Me to you or A to B?
Next door to infinity?
A message, a message!
I've got to send a message today!

(communication sound effects)

D. S. for Verses 3 and 4   **CODA**

(communication sound effects)

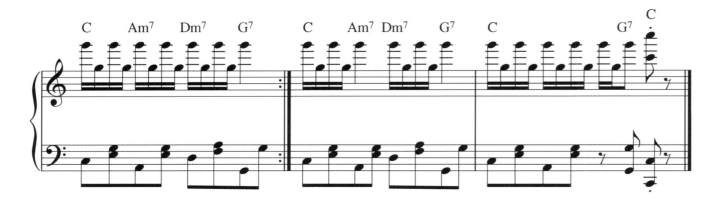

nonsense news

CD TRACK 22

Words and music: **Stephen Chadwick** (arranged for piano by Stephen Chadwick and Michael Haslam)

Give me news, news, news!
Read all about it
In a paper, or a magazine.
Give me news, news, news!
Read all about it
On your mobile phone,
  or computer screen.
Give me news, news, news!
Give me nonsense news!
What's the headline,
  what's the story?
Give me news, news, news!
Give me nonsense news!
Something cute or something gory?

Dancing dog fandangos with a frog!
  Woof, Woof, ri-dip.
Gorgeous ghost was seen
  eating toast!
  Munch, munch, whoooo.
Steve the stylish sheep kidnaps
  Little Bo Peep!
  Baa, baa, ahhh.
Eating ostrich eggs gives you
  longer legs!
  Chomp, chomp, whooop.
That's today's nonsense news!

Give me news, news, news...

Man named Matt attacked
   by killer cat!
     Me-oooow, me-ooow, ahhhh!
Chimpanzee passes GCSE!
     Eeek, eeek, oooh!
Aliens from Mars caught
   driving stolen cars!
     Brrm, brrm, beedy beedy!
Two kangaroos catch a double
   dose of flu!
     Boing, boing, achoo!

That's today's nonsense news!

Give me news, news, news!...

Give me news, news, news!
News!

Ozzie-oooo!

CD TRACK 23

Words and music: Helen MacGregor

Chant:

Kangaroo goes boing, boing!
Bandicoot goes booo!
Platypus just makes a fuss
But I don't mind 'cause I'm

Sing:

Going to a barbie,
Swimming in a billabong,
Climbing up a gum tree,
Singing a song.
Ozzie-oooo!

(repeat once)

SINGING EXPRESS SONGBOOK 3 © 2011 A&C BLACK PUBLISHERS   www.singingexpress.co.uk

I got kicked by a kangaroo

CD TRACK 24

Words and music: **traditional** (arranged for piano by Helen MacGregor and Michael Haslam)

I got kicked by a kangaroo,
I got kicked by a kangaroo,
  Kanga- kanga- roo roo roo,
  Kanga- kanga- roo roo roo,
I got kicked by a kangaroo.

I got bitten by a bandicoot...
  Bandi- bandi- coot coot coot...
I got bitten by a bandicoot.

I got pushed by a platypus...
  Platy- platy- puss puss puss...
I got pushed by a platypus.

I got prickled by a porcupine....
  Porcu- porcu- pine pine pine...
I got prickled by a porcupine.

I got wobbled by a wallaby...
  Walla- walla- be be be...
I got wobbled by a wallaby.

They sent me back to Bendigo...
  Bendi- bendi- go go go...
They sent me back to Bendigo.

I got cuddled by a koala bear...
  Koala -oala bear bear bear...
I got cuddled by a koala bear.

NB: The recording of this song uses the keys of B♭ (vv 1 & 2), C (vv 3 & 4), D (vv 5 & 6) and E♭ (v 7).
This version is in the key of C.

Down by the bay

CD TRACK 25
Words and music: traditional

Call:
Down by the bay,

Response:
Down by the bay,

Call:
Where the watermelons grow,

Response:
Where the watermelons grow,

Call:
Back to my home,

Response:
Back to my home,

Call:
I dare not go,

Response:
I dare not go,

Call:
For if I do,

Response:
For if I do,

Response:
My mother will say ~

Response:
My mother will say ~

All:
Did you ever see a cow
with a green eyebrow,
Down by the bay?

Straight quavers

Swung quavers – reggae feel

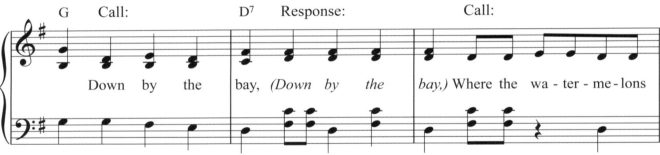

Down by the bay, (Down by the bay,) Where the wa-ter-me-lons

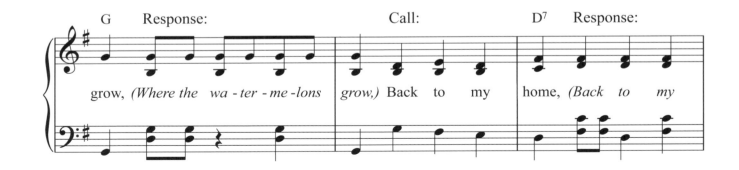

grow, (Where the wa-ter-me-lons grow,) Back to my home, (Back to my

Call: **Down by the bay...**

Response: **Down by the bay...**

   All:

**Did you ever see a bee
with a sunburned knee,
Down by the bay?**

Call: **Down by the bay...**

Response: **Down by the bay...**

   All:

**Did you ever see a whale
with a polka-dot tail,
Down by the bay?**

who did swallow Jonah?

CD TRACK 26

Words and music: **traditional**

Leader: Group:
Who did? Who did?
Who did? Who did?
All:
Who did swallow Jo Jo Jo Jo?

Leader: Group:
Who did? Who did?
Who did? Who did?
All:
Who did swallow Jo Jo Jo Jo?

Leader: Group:
Who did? Who did?
Who did? Who did?
All:
Who did swallow Jo Jo Jo Jo?

Leader: Group:
Who did Who did
swallow Jonah? swallow Jonah?
All:
Who did swallow Jonah
Down, down, down, down?

Whale did... whale did...
Whale did swallow Jo Jo Jo Jo...
Whale did swallow Jonah
Down, down, down, down.

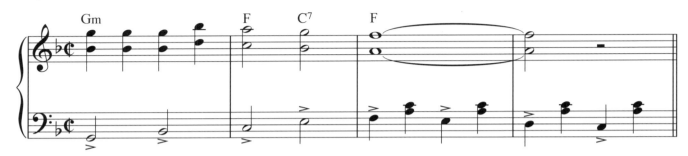

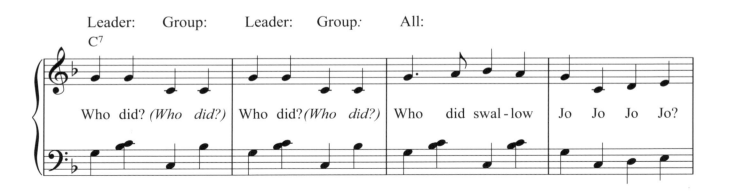

Daniel... Daniel...
  Daniel in the li li li li...
  Daniel in the lion's
  Den, den, den, den.

Noah... Noah...
  Noah in the arky arky...
  Noah in the arky
  Bailed, bailed, bailed, bailed.

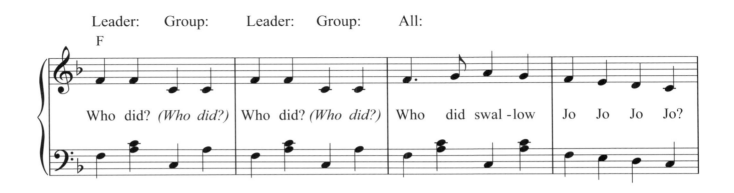

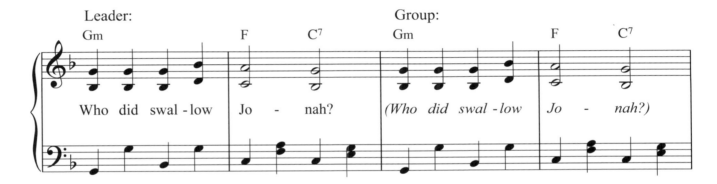

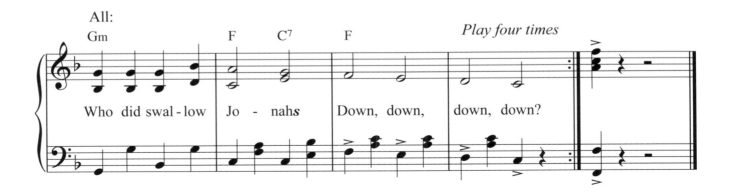

The green grass grew all around

CD TRACK 27

Words and music: **William Jerome and Harry von Tilzer** (arranged for piano by Michael Haslam)

There was a tree, a beautiful tree,
The most beautiful tree
  you ever did see.
The tree was in the ground,
  And the green grass grew,
  The green grass grew,
  The green grass grew all around.

Now on that tree, there was a branch,
The most beautiful branch
  you ever did see.
The branch was on the tree,
The tree was in the ground,
  And the green grass grew,
  The green grass grew,
  The green grass grew all around.

Now on that branch, there was a
  twig...

Now on that twig, there was a nest...

Now in that nest, there was an egg...

Now in that egg, there was a bird...

And in that bird there was a song...

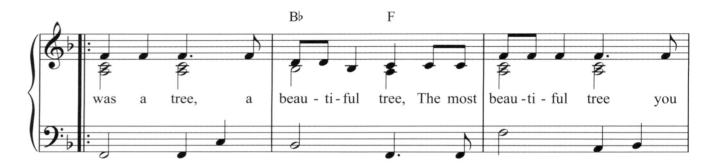

**Play once for Verse 1,
twice for Verse 2,
three times for Verse 3 etc.**

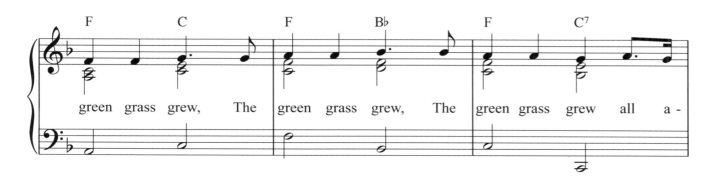

green grass grew, The green grass grew, The green grass grew all a-

1. 3. 5.

- round.   Now

2. 4. 6.

- round.   Now

Last time

- round.

Actions:

Tree: one arm held upright with outstretched fingers

Branch: hold one arm out as a branch

Twig: arm outstretched, hold up one finger

Nest: cup your hands together

Egg: make an egg shape with fingers and thumb

Bird: link thumbs to make a pair of wings

Song: make a beak open and shut with fingers and thumb

Green grass grew all around: both hands facing upwards, hands together to start, fingers wiggle, move hands away from each other representing grass growing in a semi-circle around body.

Grandma's attic

CD TRACK 28

Words and music: **Ben Glasstone**

In my Grandma's attic,
I like to look around,
To see what's hiding
In the dusty corners.
In my Grandma's attic,
I like to look around,
And you would not believe it
When I tell you what I found.

I found an old silk rug,
Inside a big blue jug.
I carefully unrolled it,
And softly down I sat,
Then that rug began to move
And guess what happened after that?
Well?
That would be telling!

In my Grandma's attic...

Inside a big, brown book,
I found a fine, red rose.
Old and dry and withered,
And very very flat,
But I gave that rose a shake
And guess what happened after that?
Well?
That would be telling!

SINGING EXPRESS SONGBOOK 3 © 2011 A&C BLACK PUBLISHERS   www.singingexpress.co.uk

In my Grandma's attic...

I found an em'rald ring,
Such a mysterious thing.
Its stone was like the eye
Of some bewitching Persian cat,
I gazed into that eye,
And guess what happened after that?
Well?
That would be telling now!

Mrs Govinda Singh

CD TRACK 29

Words and music: **David Moses** (arranged for piano by David Moses and Michael Haslam)

Mrs Govinda Singh,
Had a little shop with a sign on top.
People go out and in,
What shall we buy? Why not try?
Tea from India, very, very nice.

Mrs Govinda Singh,
Had a little shop with a sign on top.
People go out and in,
What shall we buy? Why not try?
Sandalwood perfume, (sniff – aaaahhh)
Tea from India, very, very nice.

Mrs Govinda Singh,
Had a little shop with a sign on top.
People go out and in,
What shall we buy? Why not try?
Chicken biriani, (yummmm)
Sandalwood perfume, (sniff – aaaahhh)
Tea from India, very, very nice.

Mrs Govinda Singh,
Had a little shop with a sign on top.
People go out and in,
What shall we buy? Why not try
Indian music, (ti-ka-ti-ka-tah, ti-ka-ti-ka-tah)
Chicken biriani, (yummmm)
Sandalwood perfume, (sniff – aaaahhh)
Tea from India, very, very nice.

Verse 1 jump to 1st time bar

Verse 2 jump to 2nd time bar

etc.

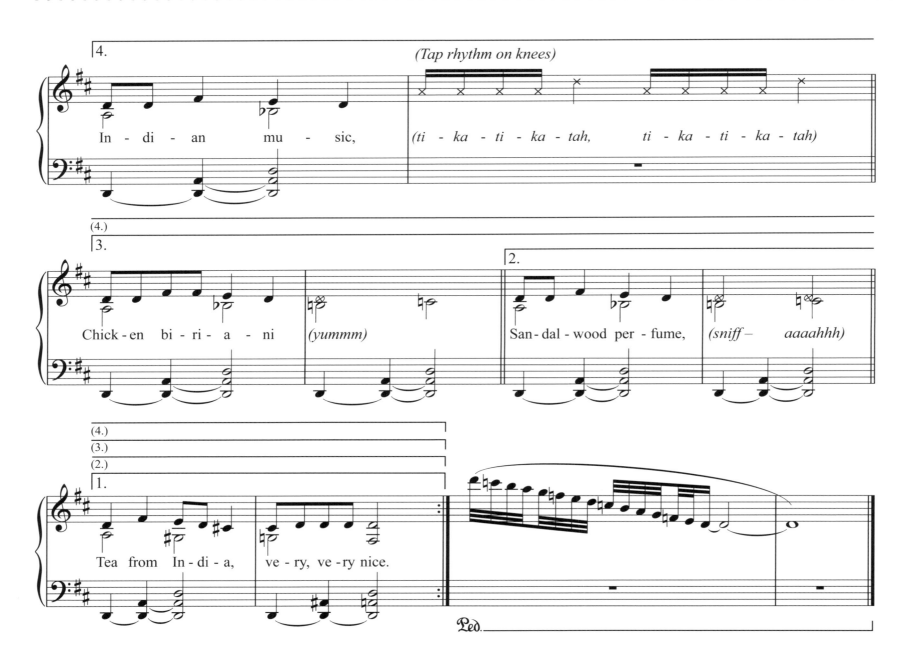

I'm a great designer

CD TRACK 30

Words and music: **Stephen Chadwick**

I'm a car designer,
Car designer,
Car designer, oh yeah!
I'm a car designer,
Car designer,
Car designer, oh yeah!
Got a job with a company,
And I'm working on products
   for the factory.
I'm a car designer,
Car designer,
A car designer, that's me!

Think for a while of a whole new style,
A car economic and green.
It's carbon and metallic, and aerodynamic,
The coolest car ever seen.
Just imagine my design,
Popping off the end
   of the production line.

   I'm a shoe designer...

Think for a while of a whole new style,
A shoe that'll flex and bend.
With multicoloured plastic,
   it's looking fantastic,
A leader in fashion trends.
Just imagine my design,
Popping off the end
   of the production line.

I'm a toy designer...

Think for a while of a whole new style,
A toy that can run and fly.
Computerised transformer,
 a speedy performer,
The smartest toy money can buy.
Just imagine my design,
Popping off the end
 of the production line.

I'm a toy designer! Yeah!

SINGING EXPRESS SONGBOOK 3 © 2011 A&C BLACK PUBLISHERS   www.singingexpress.co.uk

cool-est car e - ver seen. Just i - ma - gine my de - sign, Pop -ping

off the end of the pro -duc - tion line.____

Play three times

I'm a toy de -sign - er, Yeah!

Friends

Words and music: **Steve Grocott** (arranged for piano by Steve Grocott and Michael Haslam)

I'll be your friend ~ if you will let me,
You make me laugh ~
   that makes us happy.

  We'll run and we'll run,
  We'll lie in the sun,
  We'll have us some fun ~ won't we?
  I'll give you a ring,
  We'll swing on the swing,
  We'll do everything ~ won't we?

I'll let you join ~ what I am playing,
I'll listen to ~ what you are saying.

  We'll run and we'll run,
  We'll lie in the sun,
  We'll have us some fun ~ won't we?
  I'll give you a ring,
  We'll swing on the swing,
  We'll do everything ~ won't we?

Play song twice

Doctor, Doctor

CD TRACK 32

Words and music: **David Moses** (arranged for piano by **David Moses** and **Michael Haslam**)

Doctor, Doctor, help me, do,
I feel a bit sick, and I don't want to.
Give me a powder, give me a pill,
You always make me better
 when I feel ill.

Nurse, Nurse, help me, please,
I've got a little cough,
 and I've got a little sneeze.
I got soaked, I think I caught a chill,
You always make me better
 when I feel ill.

Dear Mr Dentist, don't hang about,
My tooth's gone wobbly,
 and it might fall out.
Give them all a polish
 with your high speed drill,
You always make me better
 when I feel ill.

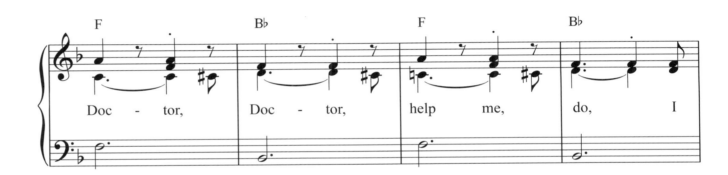

Doc - tor, Doc - tor, help me, do, I

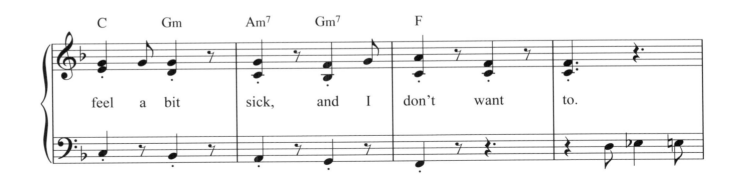

feel a bit sick, and I don't want to.

 SINGING EXPRESS SONGBOOK 3 © 2011 A&C BLACK PUBLISHERS

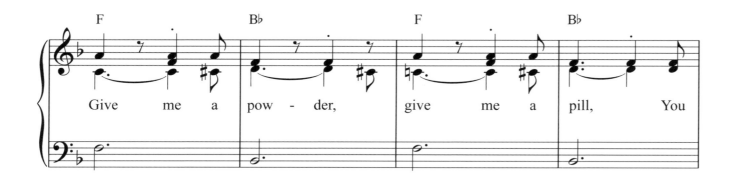

Give me a pow - der, give me a pill, You

Play three times

al - ways make me bet - ter when I feel ill.

The Tudors!

Words and music: **Val and David Machell**

The Tudors! The Tudors!
 Now everybody sings!
The Tudors! The Tudors!
 Those merry Queens and Kings!
Those merry Queens and Kings!

First came Henry Bolingbroke,
A lad from Wales of course.
Fought King Richard (with his hunch),
Who died when he lost his horse,
 His horse, his horse,
He died when he lost his horse.

Then came Henry number eight,
Who needed a son and heir.
Two of six wives
 got heads chopped off,
(Which didn't seem quite fair,
 Not fair, not fair,
It didn't seem quite fair).

The Tudors! The Tudors...

Edward was the next to reign,
A sickly little lad.
Did his best but died quite soon,
And went to join his Dad,
 His dad, his dad,
He went to join his Dad.

SINGING EXPRESS SONGBOOK 3 © 2011 A&C BLACK PUBLISHERS

Mary Tudor's greatest wish,
Was turning back to Rome.
Wed herself to the King of Spain
(He was never much at home,
 Not home, not home,
He was never much at home).

The Tudors! The Tudors...

Last came Liz (a plucky lass),
Who cleared up all the mess.
Shakespeare, Raleigh, Drake and all
Cried, 'God save Good Queen Bess!
 Queen Bess, Queen Bess!'
Cried, 'God save Good Queen Bess!'

The Tudors! The Tudors...

VERSE

First came Hen-ry Bo-ling-broke, A lad from Wales of course. Fought King Rich-ard

(with his hunch), Who died when he lost his horse, His horse, his horse, He

1. 3.
died when he lost his horse.

2. 4. 5.
fair.

D. S.

The

SINGING EXPRESS SONGBOOK 3 © 2011 A&C BLACK PUBLISHERS   www.singingexpress.co.uk

The bebop ballad of Boudicca

CD TRACK 34

Words and music: **Suzy Davies** (arranged for piano by Suzy Davies and Michael Haslam)

Chant:

Buh-buh-buh buh Boudicca,
  Buh-buh-buh buh Boudicca,
Buh-buh-buh buh Boudicca,
  Buh-buh Boudicca.

Sing:

There was a queen in days of old,
When it came to war,
  there was none so bold.
She ruled some Celts, a fearsome bunch,
Then came the Romans,
  then came the crunch.
  (Uh-oh!)

Chant 1 (the Romans):

Roman army (x7)

Chant 2 (the Romans):

Emperor (clap clap clap)

  Claudius (clap clap clap) (x 2 1/2)

Chant 3 (the Celts):

  Buh-buh-buh buh Boudicca (x3)

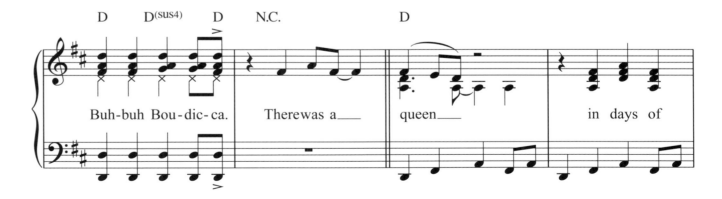

All chant:

What are the Romans? Rubbish!
Wooooaaaaah!

Sing:

They battled hard on hill and field,
They blunted swords
** and dented shields,**
Until at last the deed was done,
Iceni lost, the Romans won!
** (Boo/Hooray!)**

There was a queen in days of old,
When it came to war,
** there was none so bold.**
She ruled some Celts, a fearsome bunch,
Then came the Romans, then came the
crunch.

Chant:

Buh-buh-buh buh Boudicca,
** Buh-buh-buh buh Boudicca,**
Buh-buh-buh buh Boudicca,
** Bye-bye Boudicca**
(Yeah!)

SINGING EXPRESS SONGBOOK 3 © 2011 A&C BLACK PUBLISHERS   www.singingexpress.co.uk

Acknowledgements

The authors and publishers would like to thank the following for their generous support and advice in the preparation of **Singing Express 3**:

Philip Ashby, Chris Bartram, Em Whitfield Brooks, James Bachmann, Stephen Chadwick, Kim Chandler, Jacqui Doughty, Christiane Engel, Jon Finnigan, Barry Gibson, Ben Glasstone, Steve Grocott, Michael Haslam, Matthew Holmes, Jason Lane, Jocelyn Lucas, Val and David Machell, Paloma Gomez Martinez, Matthew Moore, David Moses, Sue Nicholls, Nigel Pilkington, Jeanne Roberts, Ian Shepherd, Saffron Stocker, Kate Stonham, Anthony Strong, Doreen Thorogood, Kaye Umansky, David Weston, Matthew White and Kirsty Young.

All works by Ana Sanderson (AS), Gillyanne Kayes (GK), Jeremy Fisher (JF), Helen MacGregor (HM) and Maureen Hanke (MH) were written by the authors for **Singing Express 3**; © administered by A&C Black Publishers.

The works by writers listed below were selected/written for **Singing Express 3** and copyright of the works is administered by A&C Black Publishers:
Em Whitfield Brooks for **Just two feet**.
Stephen Chadwick for **Traffic jamming**, **No home for the polar bear**, **Noisy vintage car**, **Nonsense news**, **I'm a great designer**.
Barry Gibson for **Singing all day**, **Dot to dot**, **Who's that lurking in the log pile?**, **Doodle oodle oodle**, **Sing bird**, **A message**.
Ben Glasstone for **Grandma's attic**.
Steve Grocott for **Friends**.
Val and David Machell for **The Tudors!**
David Moses for **Circle song**, **What a load of rubbish**, **We're on the move**, **Fancy Anansi**, **Mrs Govinda Singh**.
Matthew White and **Ana Sanderson** for **Done it**.

The copyright holders of the following works have granted their permission for the inclusion of their works in **Singing Express 3**:
Helen MacGregor for **Big bad bug**, **Mirror, mirror**, **I got kicked by a kangaroo**.
David Moses for **Doctor, Doctor**.
Sue Nicholls for **Neighbours**.

The works by writers listed below are included from other A&C Black publications: © administered by A&C Black Publishers:
Suzy Davies for **The bebop ballad of Boudicca**.

All audio performances were created specially for **Singing Express 3** and are copyright A&C Black Publishers. The authors and Publishers thank the following for their work:

Vocalists/Presenters: Rosemary Amoani, Kim Chandler, Jeremy Fisher, Nigel Pilkington, Bridgitta Roy, Kaz Simmons, Anthony Strong, Matthew White.
Live backing instrumentalists: rock kit – Jon Finnigan.

Studio backings: **James Bachmann** (Circle song, Just two feet, Chocolate, molinillo, Down by the bay, The green grass grew all around), **Barry Gibson** (Singing all day, Dot to dot, What a load of rubbish, Who's that lurking in the logpile?, Doodle oodle oodle, We're on the move, Sing bird, Neighbours, A message, Doctor, Doctor), **Ben Glasstone** (Grandma's attic), **Steve Grocott** (Big bad bug, Jim along Josie, I got kicked by a kangaroo, Friends), **Chris Hussey** (The bebop ballad of Boudicca), **Matthew Moore** (Mirror, mirror, Who did swallow Jonah?), **David Moses** (Fancy Anansi, Mrs Govinda Singh).

All other studio backings including those to his own original songs were created by **Stephen Chadwick.**

Every effort has been made to trace and acknowledge copyright holders. If any right has been omitted the Publishers offer their apologies and will rectify any error in subsequent editions following notification in writing by the copyright holder.